A Penny-Farthing Productions, Inc. Book

Copyright © 2017 by Penny-Farthing Productions, Inc.

All characters in this book are fictitious. Any resemblance to actual events, institutions, or persons, living or dead, is purely coincidental.

This book is protected under the copyright laws of the United States of America. Any reproduction or other unauthorized use of the material or artwork contained herein is prohibited without the express written permission of Penny-Farthing Productions, Inc.

The Hidden Loch Graphic Novel

Published by Penny-Farthing Productions, Inc.

One Sugar Creek Center Blvd.,

Suite 820

Sugar Land, Texas 77478

(713) 780-0300 or (800) 926-2669

corp@pfproductions.com

www.pfproductions.com

987654321

ISBN: 978-0-9991709-1-5 (hardcover)

ISBN: 978-0-9991709-0-8 (softcover)

Printed in China

THE HIDDEN LOCH CREATIVE TEAM

Created and Written by
Marlaine Maddux White

Pencils and Cover by
Claude St. Aubin

Inks
James Taylor

Colors
Mike Garcia

Letters
André McBride

ACKNOWLEDGEMENTS

In appreciation of their contributions
to THE HIDDEN LOCH, we would like
to acknowledge writer and fellow
storyteller, Brian Nissen; Advisor
Jonathan Estrin; Artist and character
designer, Aaron Blaise; and Artist
and character designer, Mike Lopez.
Producing this book was a process
touched by many creative talents
and we want to extend our sincere
thanks to each person involved in
bringing it to life.

PENNY-FARTHING PRODUCTIONS, INC.

Publisher
Ken White, Jr.

Editor-in-Chief
Marlaine Maddux White

Creative Director
Trainor Houghton

Senior Editor
Jamie Luu Murphy

Project Director
Courtney Huddleston

Graphic Designer
André McBride

Marketing Coordinator
Julia Ahadi

Director Of Operations
Pam Johnston

Accounts Manager
Selma Medina

THE HIDDEN LOCH

I dedicate this story to my
beloved grandchildren:

Harrison,
Marlie,
Emma,
Dashiell,
Quillan,
Maddux,
and Seraffina

-Marlaine

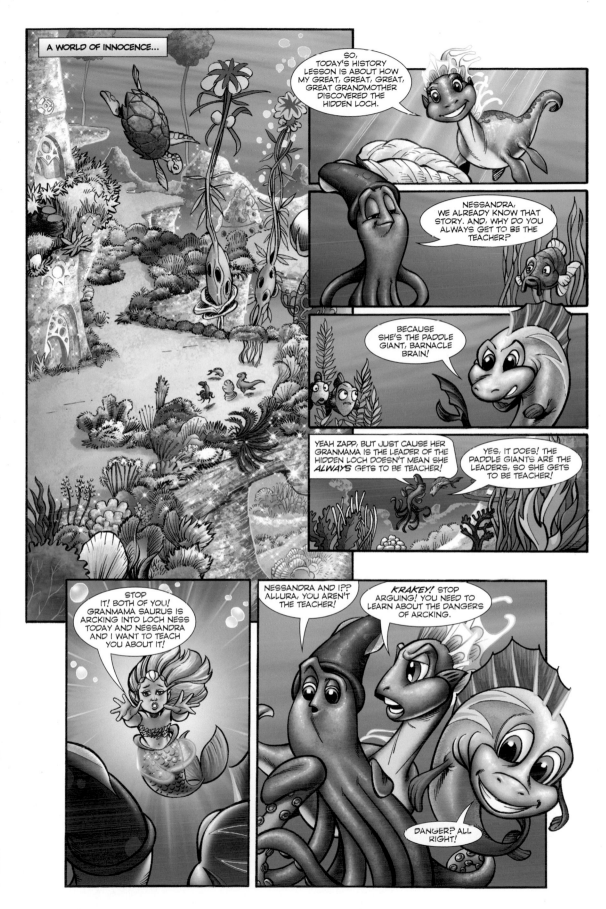

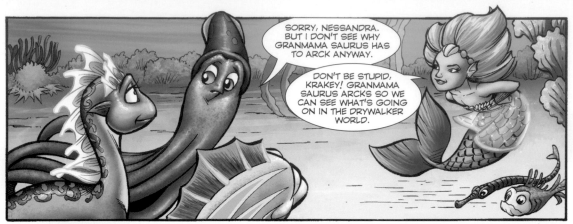

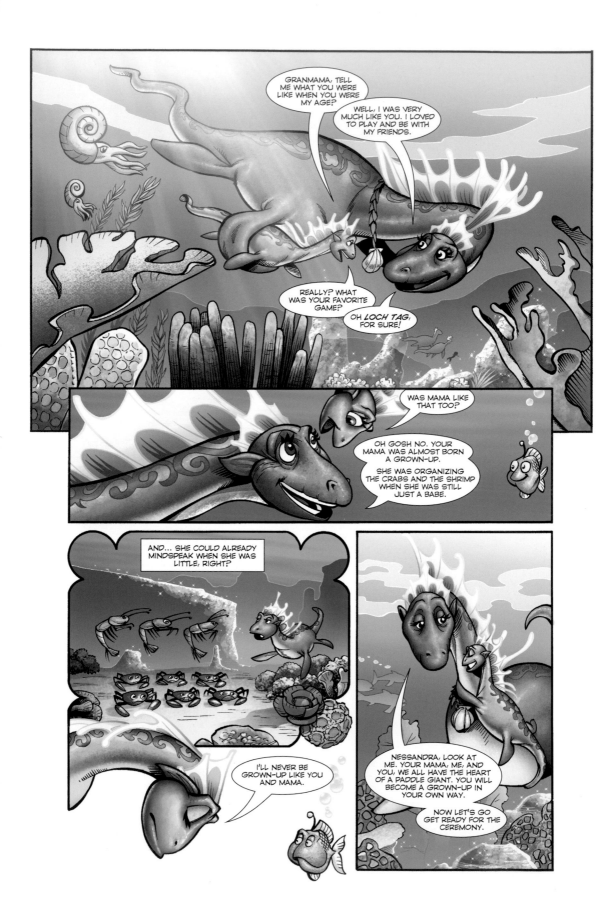

THE RITE OF ARCKING

A SACRED AND CEREMONIAL RITUAL IN WHICH THE LEADING MATRIARCHAL PLESIOSAUR OF THE HIDDEN LOCH "ARCKS," OR VENTURES INTO LOCH NESS TO GATHER IMPORTANT INFORMATION ABOUT THE OUTSIDE WORLD.

MANY YEARS AGO, WHEN THE EARTH WAS UNDERGOING CATASTROPHIC CHANGES, PLESIOSAURS, ALSO KNOWN AS PADDLE GIANTS, DISCOVERED A VAST CONCEALED CAVERN BENEATH LOCH NESS. THEY CREATED A SAFE HAVEN, WHICH THEY CALLED *THE HIDDEN LOCH*, FOR ANY CREATURE SEEKING SANCTUARY FROM THE DANGEROUS WORLD OUTSIDE.

FOR FEAR OF DISCOVERY BY THE OUTSIDE WORLD, NO OTHER CREATURE IN THE HIDDEN LOCH DARES GO INTO THE WATERS ABOVE, INTO LOCH NESS.

WITH THE FULL SUPPORT OF THE COUNCIL OF AGES, A COMMITTEE OF ANCIENT WISE CREATURES, ONLY THE EXISTING PLESIOSAUR MATRIARCH WILL PERFORM THE RITE OF ARCKING. COMMUNICATING BACK TO ANOTHER FEMALE PLESIOSAUR TELEPATHICALLY, CALLED *"MINDSPEAK"*, THEY RELAY INFORMATION ABOUT WHAT THEY SEE.

IT IS A HEAVY RESPONSIBILITY THAT ALL PLESIOSAUR MATRIARCHS HAVE SHOULDERED IN ORDER TO ACCURATELY GAUGE WHAT IS GOING ON IN THE WORLD ABOVE AND HOW IT MAY AFFECT THE FATE OF ALL WHO LIVE IN THE HIDDEN LOCH.

OUTSIDE COUNCIL HALL

I... I'M GOING BACK.

NO. WE GOTTA SEE HER GO IN!

BUT WE COULD GET IN SUPER BIG TROUBLE. LIKE... YOU-KNOW-WHO.

BENTHA?

YOU SAID HER NAME!

BENTHA! BENTHA! BENTHA!

DON'T WORRY, KRAKEY. I'LL PROTECT YOU. BESIDES, GRANMAMA BANISHED BENTHA - SO SHE WON'T BE COMING BACK!

HOW COME ONLY YOU GUYS GET TO GO UP THERE?

CUZ WE JUST DO!

12

GRANMAMA ENTERING LOCH NESS

MAMA!

WHAT IS IT? TELL US!

WHAT'S WRONG...?

GRANMAMA??

IS GRAN SAURUS IN DANGER?

YES, SHE'S BEEN *ATTACKED!*

OH NO, *DRYWALKERS!*

I'M COMING, MAMA!

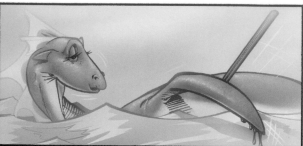

OPEN YOUR EYES, MAMA. DO NOT SLEEP.

DO NOT SLEEP!

LOWER HER GENTLY, BIG NESS!

GRANMAMA!

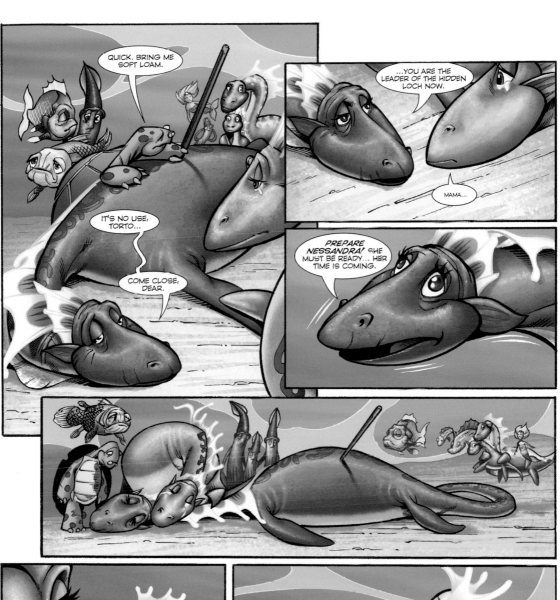

THE VAST AND BEAUTIFUL
HIDDEN LOCH IS IN MOURNING...

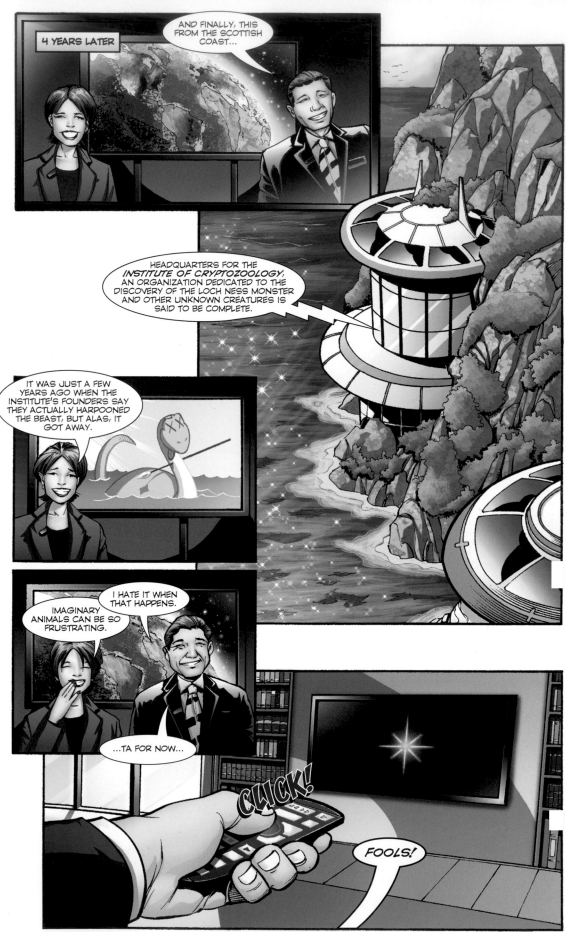

22

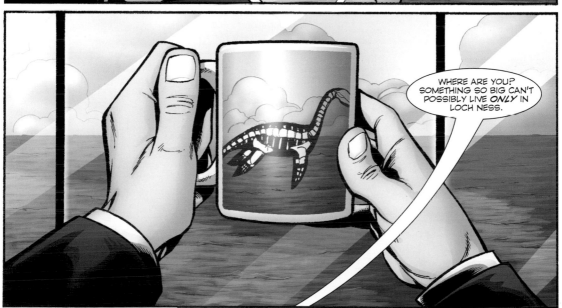

ALLURA! COME PLAY WITH US.

LOCH TAG? REALLY?

NOT INTERESTED.

NESSANDRA, WON'T YOU PLAY LOCH TAG WITH US...LIKE YOU USED TO?

I CAN'T. I HAVE TO BE GROWN-UP NOW AND ACT LIKE A PADDLE GIANT.

OH RIGHT! YOU HAVE TO DO YOUR FIRST ARCK SOON... ARE YOU SCARED?

I DON'T WANNA TALK ABOUT IT!

...AND YOU CAN'T EVEN MINDSPEAK YET.

KRAKEY! THANKS FOR REMINDING ME!

SORRY...

YOU SHOULD BE! I'M DOING THE BEST I CAN!

24

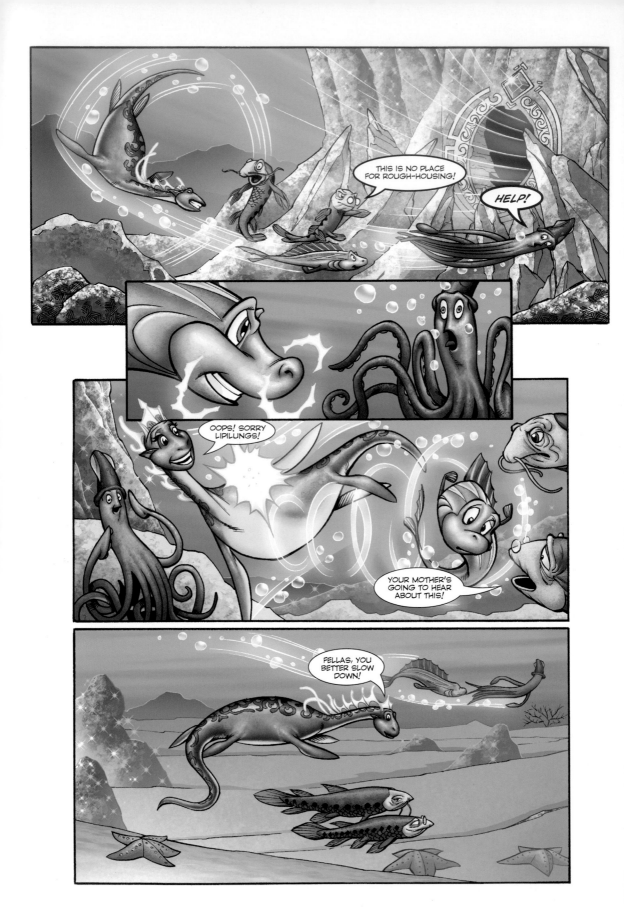

ZAPP!

NESSANDRA!

THE NEPTUNE TUNNEL!

THEY'LL BE SUCKED IN!

GASP!

GOT 'EM!

THRUMP!

PULL!

WHEW!

OKAY... YOU'RE "IT"...?

WHEN WILL YOU GET CONTROL OF YOUR DAUGHTER, WYNDA?!

PADDLE GIANT POINT

I MISS YOU, GRANMAMA. I WISH WE COULD TALK.

I'M NOT SURE I CAN ARCK, GRANMAMA. I WANT TO – BUT I CAN'T EVEN STAY OUT OF TROUBLE – LET ALONE BRING KNOWLEDGE OF THE DRYWALKERS TO THE HIDDEN LOCH.

AND YOU'RE WHINY.

GO AWAY, ALLURA.

YOU SHOULD BE *HONORED* TO ARCK, INSTEAD OF COMPLAINING ABOUT IT. YOU'RE MORE JELLYFISH THAN PADDLE GIANT.

... AND YOU'RE MORE *DRYWALKER* THAN LOCH DWELLER!

I'M SORRY, ALLURA, YOU KNOW I DIDN'T MEAN THAT!

WHAT'S HAPPENED TO US, ALLURA? SINCE THE DAY YOU WERE FOUND AND BROUGHT HERE WE'VE BEEN SISTERS AND BEST FRIENDS. BUT EVER SINCE GRANMAMA DIED...YOU'VE SEEMED DIFFERENT.

I MISS OUR CLOSENESS, DON'T YOU?

...YES.

OH, ALLURA, I REALLY NEED YOUR HELP.

OKAY...?

I'M THINKING... ABOUT SNEAKING INTO LOCH NESS.

WHAT?!

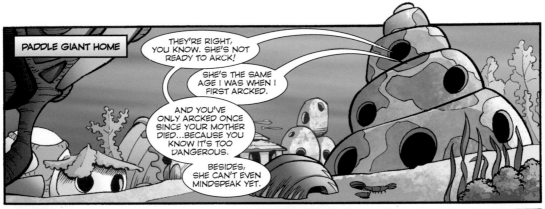

PADDLE GIANT HOME

THEY'RE RIGHT, YOU KNOW. SHE'S NOT READY TO ARCK!

SHE'S THE SAME AGE I WAS WHEN I FIRST ARCKED.

AND YOU'VE ONLY ARCKED ONCE SINCE YOUR MOTHER DIED...BECAUSE YOU KNOW IT'S TOO DANGEROUS.

BESIDES, SHE CAN'T EVEN MINDSPEAK YET.

SHE SAW HER GRANMAMA DIE, DEAR. AND NOW SHE'S FILLED WITH FEAR. SHE WON'T MINDSPEAK UNTIL THOSE SCARS ARE HEALED.

BUT –

MY MOTHER WAS RIGHT. NESSANDRA HAS SOME SPECIAL PURPOSE.

ALL THE ONES WHO HAVE PASSED ON ARE URGING ME TO PREPARE HER QUICKLY. I CAN FEEL IT. NESSANDRA MAY BE IN LINE TO COMPLETE THE "KNOWLEDGE JOURNEY" AS HER GREAT GRAN DID –

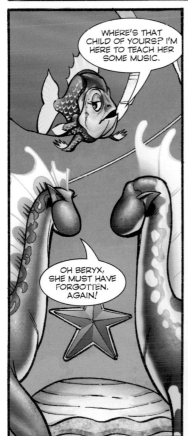

WHERE'S THAT CHILD OF YOURS? I'M HERE TO TEACH HER SOME MUSIC.

OH BERYX, SHE MUST HAVE FORGOTTEN. AGAIN!

MINDSPEAK HER HOME, THEN.

OH, SORRY... I FORGOT.

I'LL... GO FIND HER MYSELF.

34

THE LAST THING WE NEED IS *YOU* SHOCKING A DRYWALKER.

GULP... IT'S UP TO ME!

A LITTLE HELP, YOUNG MAN.

WHY'D SHE DO THAT?!

WHO KNOWS? POOR CHILD! WE HAVE TO GET HER OUT OF THERE!

I'LL DO IT!

NO, NO, NO...

WAIT!

THERE WAS NO CHOICE! WE GOTTA FIND NESSANDRA BEFORE THE DRYWALKERS DO!

WHAT'LL THEY DO TO HER IF SHE'S CAPTURED?!

STOP IT! BOTH OF YOU! *NO ONE'S* GETTING CAPTURED!

...SHE'LL COME RIGHT OUT, AND GET IN A LITTLE TROUBLE...THAT'S ALL!

I'VE GOTTA FIND MAMA AND PAPA.

LOCH NESS

GASP...
THAT'S WHAT KILLED
GRANMAMA!

DRYWALKERS?!

NESSANDRA!

OH, DEAR.

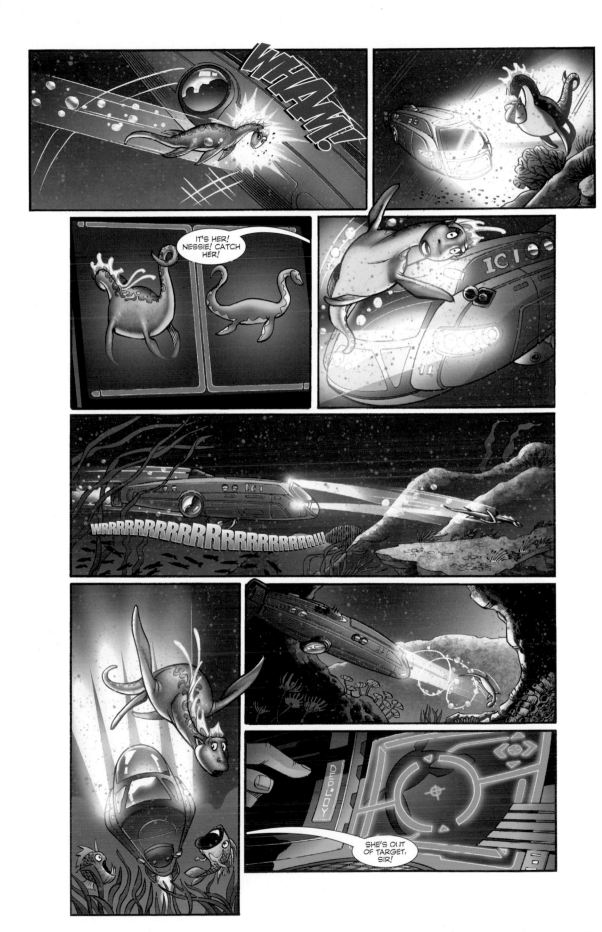

40

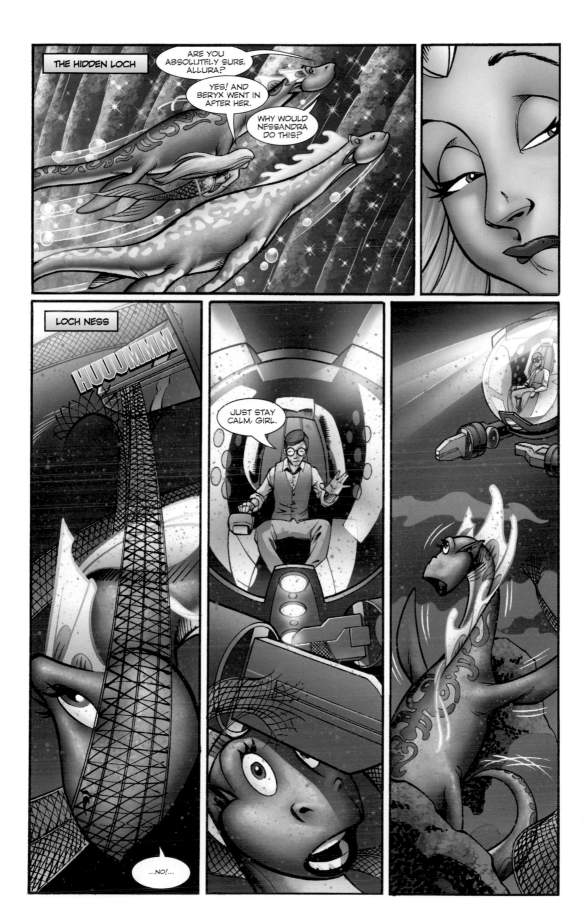

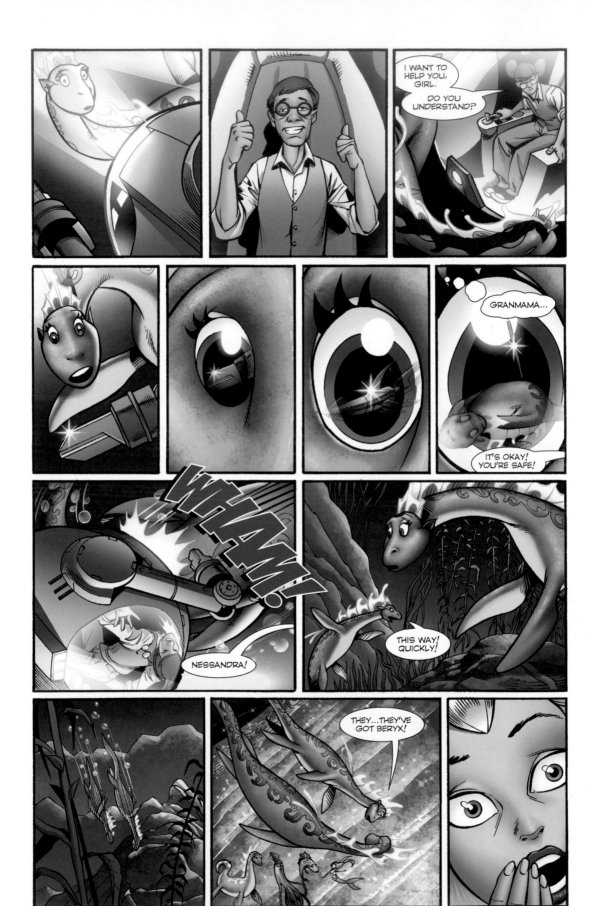

WE'VE GOT COMPETITION!

WE *MUST* DISCOVER WHERE THIS CAPROBYREX CAME FROM...ALONG WITH HER PLESIOSAUR FRIEND.

PERHAPS YOU WILL SHOW US THE WAY?

YOU'LL SHARE YOUR SECRET, WON'T YOU, DEARIE?

NOT IF I CAN HELP IT!

WHO KNOWS WHAT ELSE IS DOWN THERE!

BUT IT APPEARS WE'RE IN A RACE TO FIND IT, PEOPLE.

YES, YOU ARE.

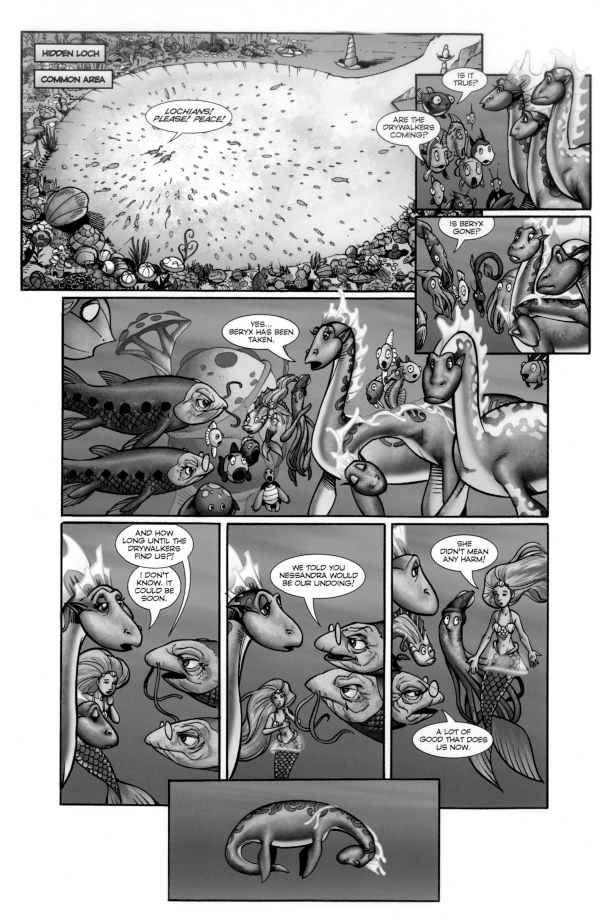

FELLOW LOCH DWELLERS, I PROPOSE—

PROPOSALS ARE A MATTER FOR THE COUNCIL AND THE COUNCIL ONLY!

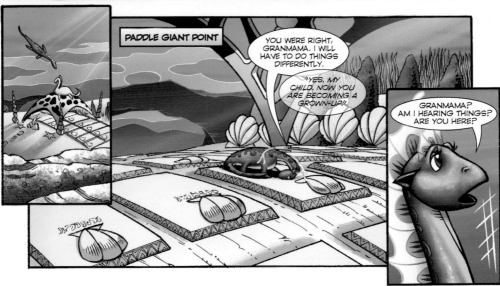

PADDLE GIANT POINT

YOU WERE RIGHT, GRANMAMA. I WILL HAVE TO DO THINGS DIFFERENTLY.

"YES, MY CHILD. NOW YOU ARE BECOMING A GROWN-UP!"

GRANMAMA? AM I HEARING THINGS? ARE YOU HERE?

COUNCIL HALL

I PROPOSE THAT NESSANDRA'S RITE OF ARCKING BE POSTPONED. INDEFINITELY.

...MMMHMMM...

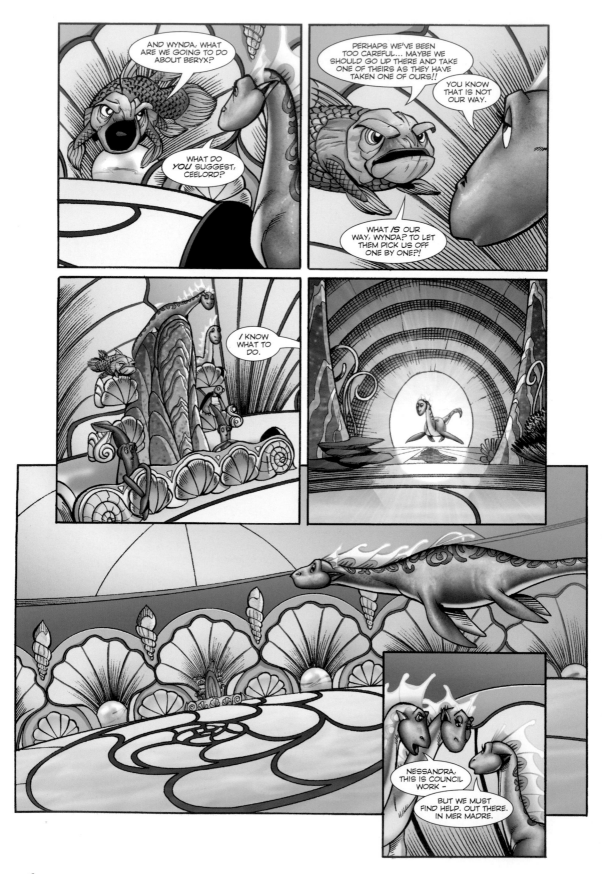

HAVEN'T WE HAD ENOUGH BOLD IDEAS FOR ONE DAY, WYNDA?!

LET HER SPEAK.

WE ALWAYS TALK ABOUT THOSE WHO LIVE IN MER MADRE AS NOT HAVING OUR ANCIENT BLOODLINES AND AS BEING STRANGERS, AND MAYBE THEY ARE...BUT...

WHAT ARE YOU SAYING?

THEY ARE ALSO OUR FELLOW SEA CREATURES! AND WOULDN'T THEY BE THREATENED BY DRYWALKERS TOO? WOULDN'T THEY HELP US?

NESSANDRA –

GRANMAMA TOLD ME MANY TIMES THAT IF THE HIDDEN LOCH WAS TO SURVIVE WE WOULD HAVE TO DO THINGS DIFFERENTLY. I NEVER KNEW WHAT SHE MEANT UNTIL NOW.

NESSANDRA, YOUR HEART SO GOOD, BUT –

BEFORE GRANMAMA DIED, TORTO, WHAT DID SHE SAY?

"GET NESSANDRA READY. SHE FIND ANSWERS."

I'VE NEVER BEEN SO SURE OF WHAT I MUST DO. FEAR DROVE ME TO A DREADFUL MISTAKE. I WON'T LET IT STOP ME FROM GOING INTO MER MADRE TO FIND HELP.

THIS IS AN INSULT, NESSANDRA! IF GRAN SAURUS WANTED US TO DO SOMETHING SO BOLD, WHY WOULDN'T SHE TELL US?

BECAUSE SHE KNEW WE WEREN'T READY TO HEAR IT.

"WE OLD ONES HAVE A LOT OF FEAR."

SURELY YOU CAN SEE, WYNDA. THE LOCHIANS THINK OF NESSANDRA AS A TROUBLEMAKER!

SHE CAN'T EVEN MINDSPEAK.

FRIENDS!

I SHARE YOUR CONCERNS! BUT IF OUR ANCESTORS HAVE CHOSEN NESSANDRA... THEN WE HAVE TO ACCEPT THAT THIS IS THE TIME FOR THE NEXT KNOWLEDGE JOURNEY INTO MER MADRE.

THANK YOU...

THE DECISION IS MADE THEN!

ACCORDING TO ANCIENT TRADITION, IN TIMES OF THREAT, YOUNG ONES HAVE BEEN ALLOWED TO VENTURE INTO MER MADRE ON KNOWLEDGE JOURNEYS. SELECT YOUR COMPANIONS CAREFULLY... AND WE WILL PREPARE ALL OF YOU FOR THE JOURNEY.

YES, SIR.

WHAT *HAVEN'T* I SEEN?! JUST OUTSIDE THE TUNNEL THERE ARE THE CUTEST LITTLE PHOSPHORESCENT FISH!

THEY'RE SORT OF A BLUE-GREEN—

GRRRK

YOU'RE MY SPY! ACT LIKE IT!

OH. RIGHT. SORRY.

...BUT THEN THEY CHANGE TO A BRIGHT PINK!

OKAY, OKAY...THE COUNCIL HAS MADE A DECISION TO SEEK HELP IN MER MADRE.

FOOLS! WHO COULD THEY POSSIBLY SEND THAT WOULD BE A MATCH FOR ME? GRAN SAURUS MAY HAVE BANISHED ME, BUT WITH HER GONE, WHO IS STRONG ENOUGH TO FACE ME NOW?!

NO ONE IN THE HIDDEN LOCH WOULD DARE!

OH YEAH... WYNDA IS SENDING NESSANDRA TO FIND HELP.

IT'S TOO...PERFECT! WYNDA'S LITTLE PRINCESS DAUGHTER...OUT HERE? IN BIG BAD MER MADRE?

IF THE LOCHIANS WANT HER BACK ALIVE, THEY'LL HAVE TO TURN OVER THE HIDDEN LOCH TO ME!

50

52

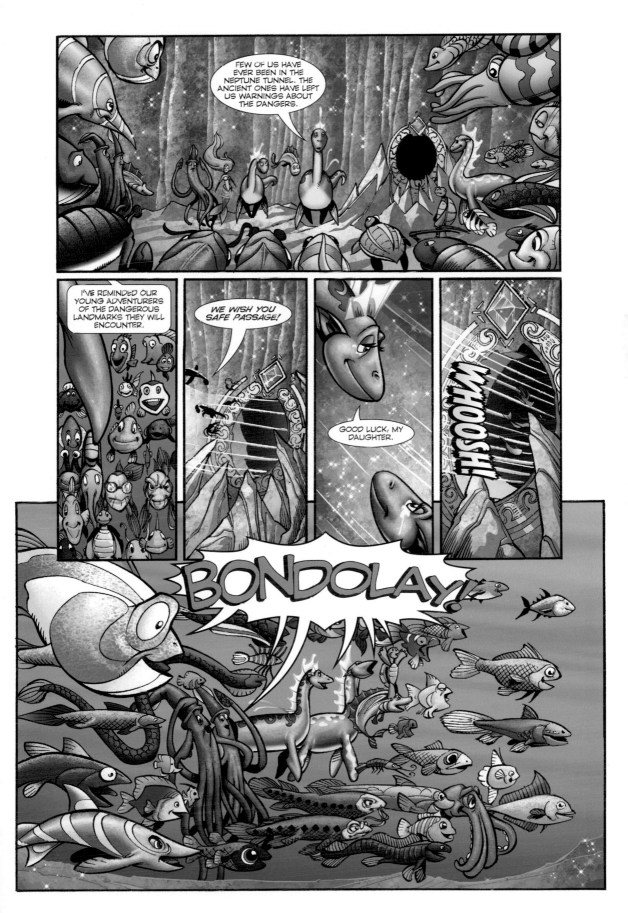

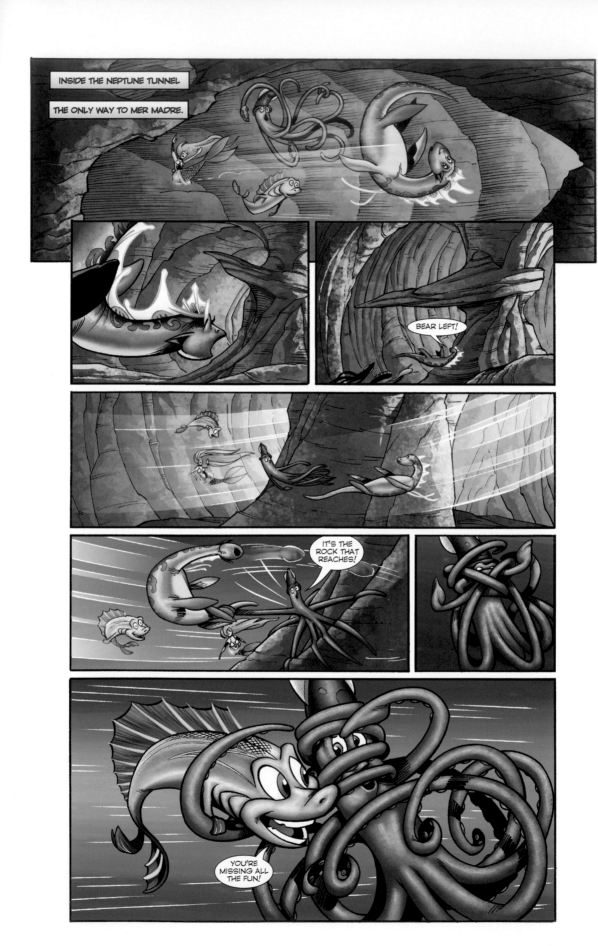

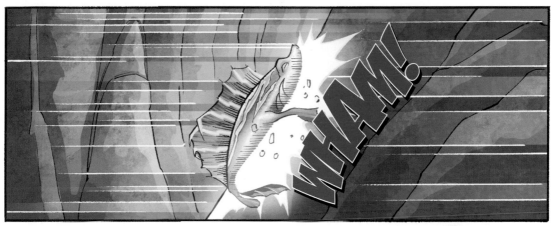

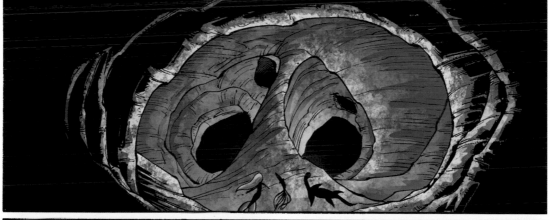

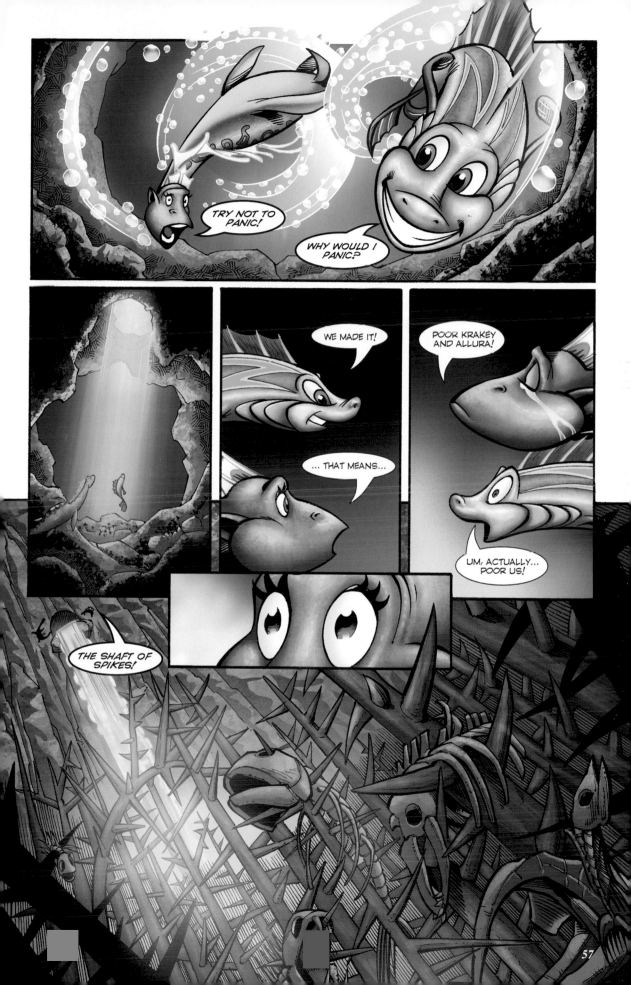

TRY NOT TO PANIC!

WHY WOULD I PANIC?

WE MADE IT!

... THAT MEANS...

POOR KRAKEY AND ALLURA!

UM, ACTUALLY... POOR US!

THE SHAFT OF SPIKES!

BOOM

ZAPP, YOU SAVED US!

YOU MADE IT!

ALLURA! KRAKEY!

I SHOULD HAVE LISTENED TO YOU ALLURA. YOU KNEW TO GO LEFT!

IT DOESN'T MATTER NOW. WE'RE ALL SAFE.

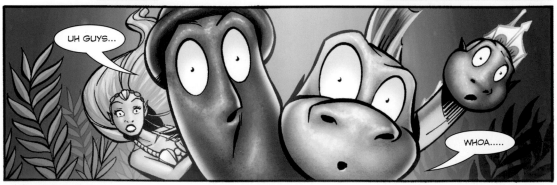

UH GUYS...

WHOA.....

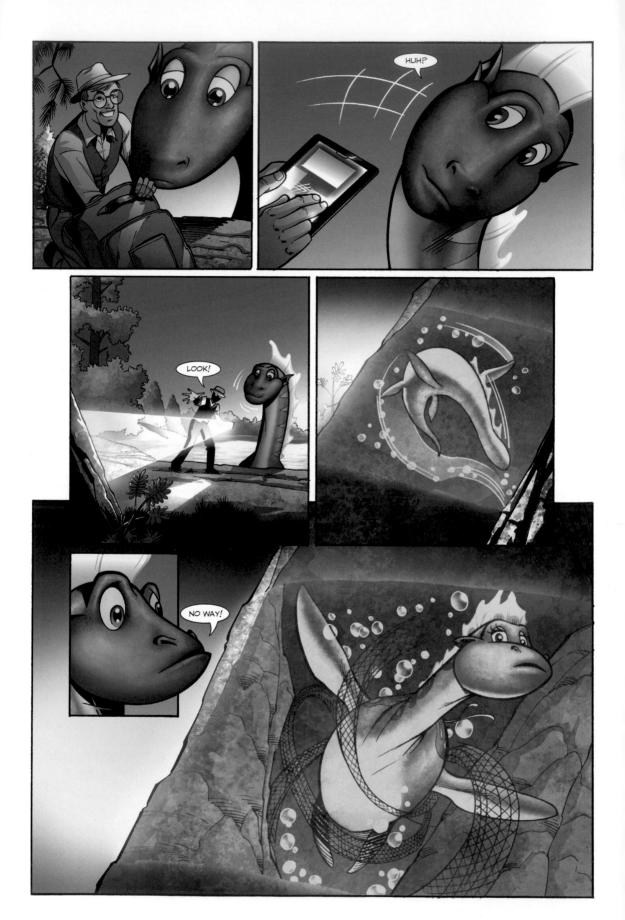

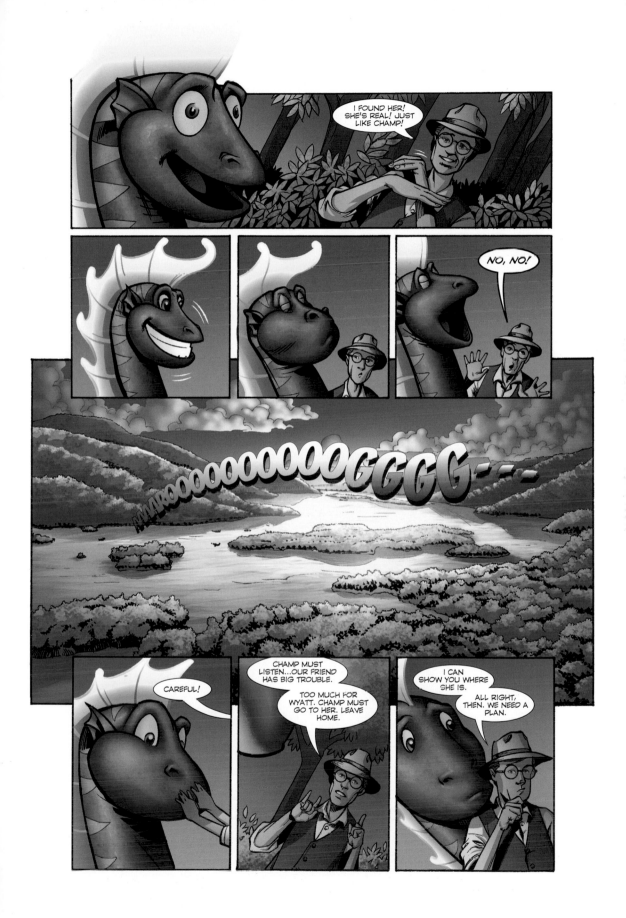

MER MADRE

SO?...CAN YOU... HELP US?

FOR TRAVELING IN SCHOOLS, THESE GUYS SURE ARE STUP—

ALLURA!!!

I KNOW! WE'LL ACT IT OUT!

OKAY. SHE. NESSANDRA. JUST SWIMMING AROUND.

LA LA LA.

ALONG COME DRYWALKER!

DRYWALKER CHASE NESSANDRA.

AAAAAH! DRYWALKER!

68

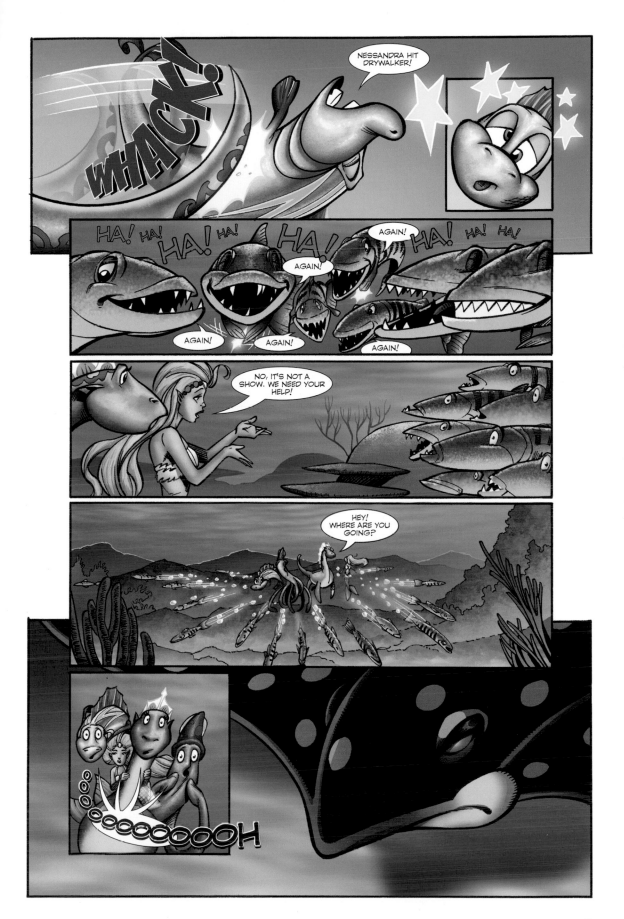

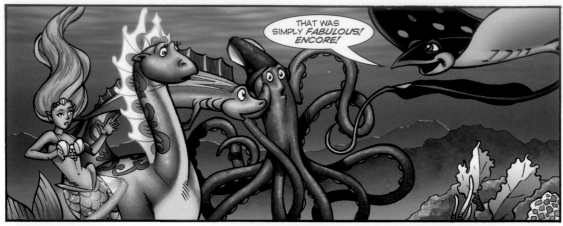

GLAD TO KNOW MY NAME STILL LIVES ON IN THE HIDDEN LOCH.

WHY WOULDN'T IT? YOU'RE THE ONLY ONE WHO EVER DEFIED GRANMAMA SAURUS.

IS THAT THE STORY THEY TELL THESE DAYS? NOTHING ELSE?

WELL, IT'S A TALE THAT'S STILL BEING WRITTEN. FINAL CHAPTER: WYNDA TURNS OVER RULE TO BENTHA AFTER HER DAUGHTER IS KIDNAPPED.

ONLY THAT YOU FAILED.

THE END.

SO, WHERE DO ALL OF YOU THINK YOU'RE GOING?

OH MY, THIS IS PERFECT!

74

A DEAD DRYWALKER?

EEEEEEEEEEEE!

WE'RE TRAPPED IN HERE!

...THAT'S RIGHT. THERE'S NO ESCAPE, NESSANDRA...BUT THERE IS A SOLUTION.

SUBMIT TO ME, AND I WILL PROMISE TO SPARE YOUR PARENTS.

I'LL GET PAST HER. SHE WON'T SEE ME.

IT'S MY KIND WHO SHOULD HAVE BEEN RULING THE HIDDEN LOCH ALL ALONG.

BECAUSE WE ARE SUPERIOR!

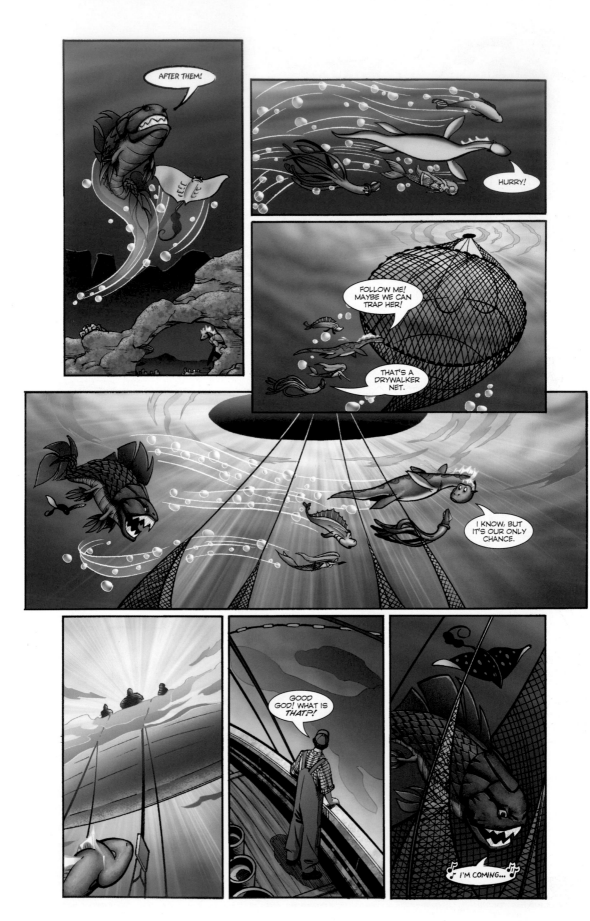

ALLURA?

THINK SHE'S JUST DOING THE INVISIBLE THING?

I SURE HOPE SO.

BUT HOW DID YOU EVEN KNOW I WAS HERE AND NEEDED HELP?

MY FRIEND, WYATT, TOLD ME.

WYATT? CAN HE HELP US STOP THE DRYWALKERS?

WELL, ACTUALLY –

PLEASE SAY YES... THE HIDDEN LOCH IS IN SO MUCH DANGER AND IT'S ALL BECAUSE OF ME.

YOU SEE, I WASN'T SUPPOSED TO GO UP TO LOCH NESS, BUT I DID! I WAS JUST SCARED, BECAUSE OF GRANMAMA!

OH NESSANDRA... WHAT DID I DO?

WHY DID THEY DO IT?

WHO?

THE DRYWALKERS! THEY KILLED GRANMAMA FOR SPORT! THEY KIDNAPPED ONE OF OUR LEADERS. AND NOW THEY MIGHT DISCOVER OUR HOME!

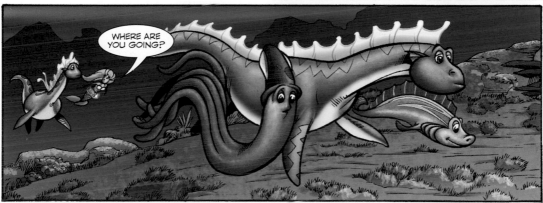

CORAL GARDEN

THE EMPERIANS ARE MIGHTY WARRIORS! THEY'D BE PERFECT PROTECTORS OF THE HIDDEN LOCH. BUT THEY'RE HARD TO FIND...LIKE MY LEARNING SHELLS. *AH!*

OH, HERE'S ONE..

SON, TODAY'S LESSON IS ABOUT EXOTIC SEA CREATURES.

EVERYTHING MY PARENTS EVER TAUGHT ME ARE IN THESE SHELLS... INCLUDING A SACRED RITUAL ON HOW TO REVEAL THE CITY OF EMPERIA.

REALLY?

THOSE TWO ARE DEFINITELY GETTING TOGETHER.

YOU THINK SO?

LEMME PUT IT THIS WAY: NO ONE EVER TOLD THOSE TWO "THERE'S OTHER FISH IN THE SEA."

LOOK CHAMP! THERE ARE THE EMPERIAN STANDING STONES YOUR FATHER TOLD YOU ABOUT.

THE ARCHWAY OF KNAVVERSHALLOM – ARCTIC WATERS

ONLY AN EMPERIAN, PURE OF HEART, CAN REVEAL THE CITY OF EMPERIA AND OPEN ITS GATES.

LET THE WORTHY EMPERIAN STAND BEFORE THE ARCHWAY OF KNAVVERSHALLOM AND SAY:

I LIED WHEN I TOLD YOU IT WAS A GOOD IDEA TO GO UP TO LOCH NESS! I KNEW IT WASN'T! I RESENTED YOU!

I *WANTED* YOU TO MAKE A MISTAKE! I *WANTED* YOU TO GET IN TROUBLE! AND I *WANTED* EVERYONE TO HATE YOU FOR IT!

YOU'VE NEVER BEEN ANYTHING BUT KIND TO ME AND I'VE RETURNED IT WITH ENVY! NO ONE EVER CARED ABOUT HOW I FELT WHEN GRANMAMA DIED. THEY ONLY WORRIED ABOUT YOU!

AND NOW THIS IS MY PUNISHMENT. I'LL NEVER KNOW WHO I AM.

I'M SO...SO SORRY.

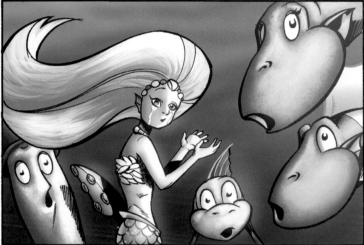

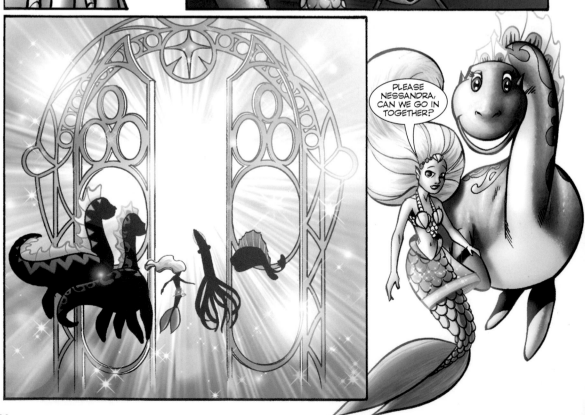

PLEASE NESSANDRA, CAN WE GO IN TOGETHER?

EMPERIAN KING'S HOME

SO, YOU SEE, ALLURA, YOU WERE A TINY GIRL AND IT WAS MY FAULT YOU WERE TAKEN. I TOOK PITY ON THE WALRUSES. I WAS TOO TRUSTING, NEVER SEEING THAT THEY WERE PLOTTING TO TAKE YOU FOR RANSOM.

I HAVE A DIM MEMORY OF BEING CHASED AND HIDING. I WAS AFRAID AND STRUGGLING AGAINST THE DEEP CURRENTS - AND THEN I WAS RESCUED. THE NEXT THING I REMEMBER I WAS IN THE HIDDEN LOCH.

WYNDA AND BIG NESS, AND ALL THE OTHERS, THEY TOOK CARE OF ME AND KEPT ME SAFE, FATHER... AND NOW IT'S OUR TURN TO HELP THEM.

...ALLURA. IT IS NOT OUR WAY TO GET INVOLVED IN THE BATTLES OF OTHERS.

OH, BUT LET NESSANDRA TELL YOU. I'M SURE ONCE YOU'VE HEARD —

ALLURA, MY PRECIOUS. THEY'RE GONE. I'VE SENT THEM ON THEIR WAY.

WHAT?

YOU'RE HOME NOW, DARLING. I CAN'T—

NO!

ALLURA!

INSTITUTE OF CRYPTOZOOLOGY

SHE MAY HAVE ESCAPED, BUT...

SHE DOESN'T KNOW WE CAN FIND HER. POOR FOOL.

GET THE VESSEL READY!

MER MADRE (ATLANTIC OCEAN) – CORAL GARDEN AREA

WHAT'S THIS? I'LL CHECK IT OUT.

HEY, AREN'T WE *BOTH* SUPPOSED TO BE ON LOOKOUT?

YOU EVER WONDER IF DRYWALKERS HAVE FEELINGS AND STUFF, OR DO THEY JUST KINDA WALK AROUND LIKE –

"FEEEED MEEEE."

KRAKEY?! *KRAKEY!*

AAGH!

SLAM!

ZAPP, WHERE ARE YOU?

CORAL GARDEN

MAYBE WE SHOULD JUST GO BACK TO THE HIDDEN LOCH BEFORE WE LOSE SOMEONE ELSE.

NO, NO. I BROUGHT THESE LEARNING SHELLS WITH ME AND LEFT THEM HERE IN CASE THEY WERE NEEDED.

HERE'S ONE OF MY DAD'S, LET'S LISTEN.

THE DRYWALKERS ARE A CURIOUS AND AGGRESSIVE SPECIES...

MAYBE NOT THAT ONE.

UGH. DRYWALKERS! WHY DO THEY HAVE TO BE SO AWFUL?

BUT WHAT ABOUT WHAT YOU SAID TO ALLURA'S FATHER? THAT WE NEED TO HELP EACH OTHER, NOT FEAR EACH OTHER.

I WASN'T TALKING ABOUT DRYWALKERS!

NESSANDRA... THERE'S SOMETHING I NEED TO TELL YOU...

ZAPP WANDERED OFF SOMEWHERE!

I'LL FIND HIM, NESSANDRA, SEE WHAT ELSE MY DAD HAS TO SAY.

SO WHAT WOULD I TELL *MY* CHILDREN AND GRANDCHILDREN, YOU KNOW, IF I EVER GOT SO LUCKY TO FIND A PADDLE GIANT GIRL?

OH CHAMP...

ONE THING I'D DO FOR SURE IS TELL THEM ALL ABOUT WYATT.

IT'S KINDA WEIRD THAT MY BEST FRIEND IS A DRYWALKER.

I'M HELPING HIM FIX THE OCEAN!

HE'S THE BEST! SOMETIMES I EVEN WISH I COULD *BE* A DRYWALKER!

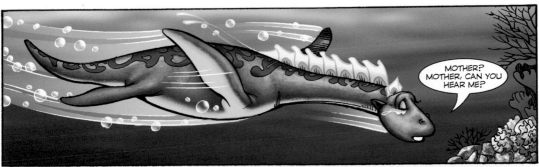

BUT...

NO! YOU TELL *LIES!* YOU SAID YOU WOULD FIGHT THE DRYWALKERS! INSTEAD, YOU'RE HELPING THEM!

NO! I MEAN, OKAY, A DRYWALKER.

YOU ARE?!

YOU EVEN SAID YOU WISHED YOU COULD *BE* ONE!

NOT ALL THE TIME. YOU KNOW, JUST, DON'T YOU EVER WISH– ?! ...LOOK, NESSANDRA, YOU'RE *WRONG* ABOUT THE DRYWALKERS –

HOW DARE YOU! THEY KILLED MY GRANDMOTHER! HOW CAN YOU SAY I'M WRONG?!

NESSANDRA, I WAS GOING TO TELL YOU...

NO! STAY AWAY. GO BACK TO YOUR DRYWALKER FRIENDS. *NEVER SPEAK TO ME AGAIN!*

...NESSANDRA ...PLEASE...

C'MON KRAKEY...

CHAMP BETRAYED US.

98

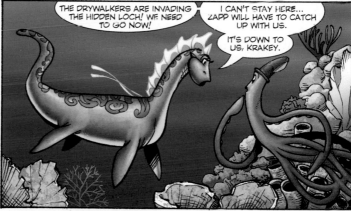

MER MADRE — CORAL GARDEN AREA

HEY! SOMEONE! ANYONE!

NESSANDRA? KRAKEY?

YOU'RE WELCOME.

WHAT HAVE I DONE? NESSANDRA AND THE HIDDEN LOCH ARE IN BIG TROUBLE.

WHAT?!

GASP!

WHO'S HURTING NESSANDRA?! I'LL FIGHT 'EM!

"CALM AND THOUGHTFUL ENERGY, ZAPP."

103

OH MY GOODNESS! IS THAT...? *BERYX!*

SHE'S FREE!

NESSANDRA! KRAKEY! WHAT ARE YOU TWO DOING HERE?!

THE HIDDEN LOCH IS IN DANGER AND WE'VE BEEN ON A MISSION TO FIND HELP.

BUT HOW DID YOU GET HERE?

WHAT! YOU'RE TELLING US THAT A DRYWALKER SET YOU FREE?!"

AS SURE AS I GOT GILLS! CALLS HIMSELF "WY-ITT". NICE FELLA. SMILES AND GOES LIKE THIS.

THAT CAN'T BE RIGHT! DRYWALKERS DON'T *HELP* US! ARE YOU SURE THE DRYWALKER SET YOU FREE?

YES, I'M SURE!

I CAN'T BELIEVE IT! YOU AND CHAMP *MUST* BE WRONG!

BUT...I'M TELLING YOU...

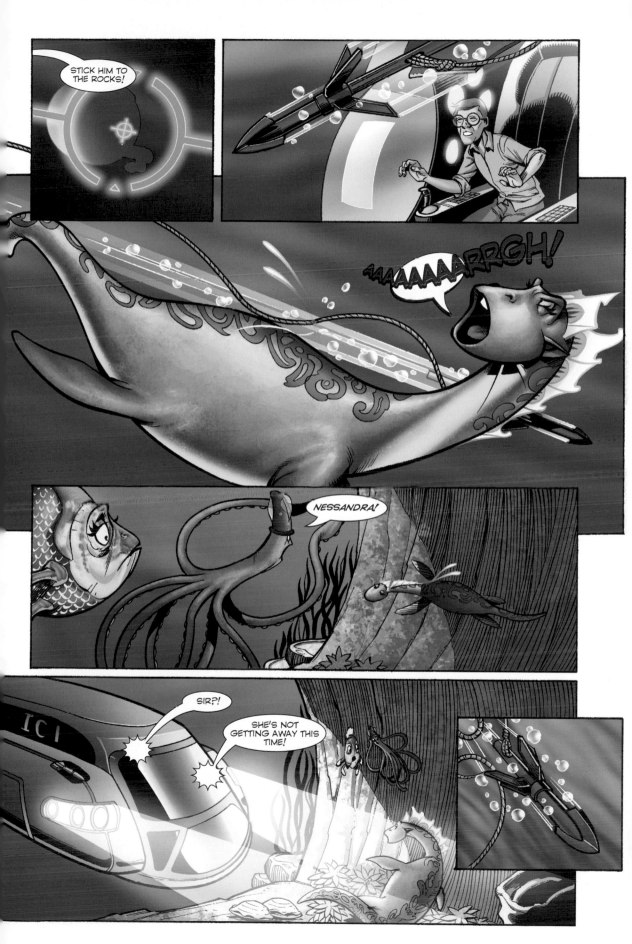

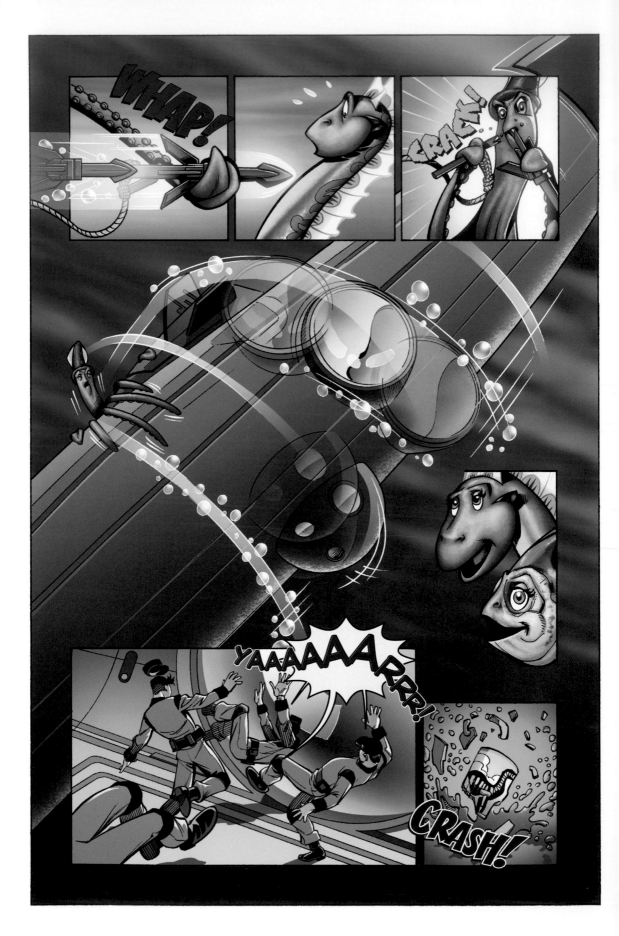

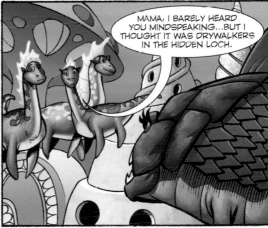

YOU WANT TO BE LED BY HER?! THIS GIRL WHO WAS SENT TO FIND HELP AND CAME HOME WITH **NOTHING!**

I WOULDN'T SAY "NOTHING".

CHAMP! YOU CAME! AND ZAPP TOO!

I HAD TO! WE'LL TALK LATER!

ANOTHER PADDLE GIANT?

ANOTHER PADDLE GIANT?

ANOTHER PADDLE GIANT?

OOH. OOOH. HOW WILL I SURVIVE? IT'S PADDLE GIANT NUMBER TWO AND HIS SIDEKICK WITH THE SPARKLES!

WHAT ARE YOU CALLING SPARKLES?

HAVE YOU FORGOTTEN WHO KNOCKED YOU OFF YOUR GAME WHEN WE LAST MET?

PURE LUCK! I'M READY FOR YOU NOW.

OH YEAH, INDIVIDUALLY YOU MAY THINK WE AREN'T MUCH –

– BUT TOGETHER...

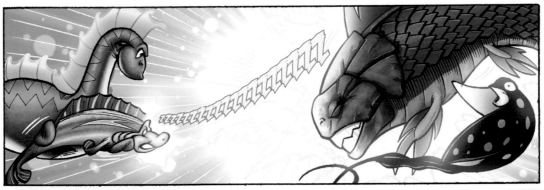

WHAT THE...

LOOKS LIKE YOUR FRIEND IS SPENT, AND I'M STILL ON FULL POWER!

NOT SO FAST, BENTHA! I'LL TAKE OVER FOR MY SON!

MOTHER...?

NESSANDRA?

YES, MOTHER IT'S ME...

BIG NESS, NESSANDRA IS MINDSPEAKING.

MOTHER, LISTEN. WE CAN'T AFFORD TO LOSE OUR WISEST LEADERS. TAKE THE COUNCIL INTO THE NEPTUNE TUNNEL!

WHAT? I CAN'T. THE TUNNEL'S TOO DANGEROUS FOR THE OLD ONES.

YES YOU CAN! STAY LEFT OF THE ROCK THAT REACHES AND RIDE THE UPPER CURRENT. YOU WILL BE FINE.

ALSO... I KNOW IT SOUNDS CRAZY BUT THERE IS A GOOD DRYWALKER OUT THERE! YOU CAN TRUST HIM! HE'LL KEEP YOU SAFE!

WHAT?! ...ALL RIGHT, IF YOU SAY SO.

LOOKS LIKE YOU'RE OUT OF AMMO, SUCKER!

OH! YOU'RE LEAVING. GOOD RIDDANCE, COWARDS! YOU'LL NEVER SURVIVE OUT THERE! THE HIDDEN LOCH IS MINE!

AND NOW, TIME TO FINISH WITH NESSANDRA'S HERO!

SURE! LET'S SEE WHAT YOU'VE GOT, BESIDES A BIG MOUTH!

114

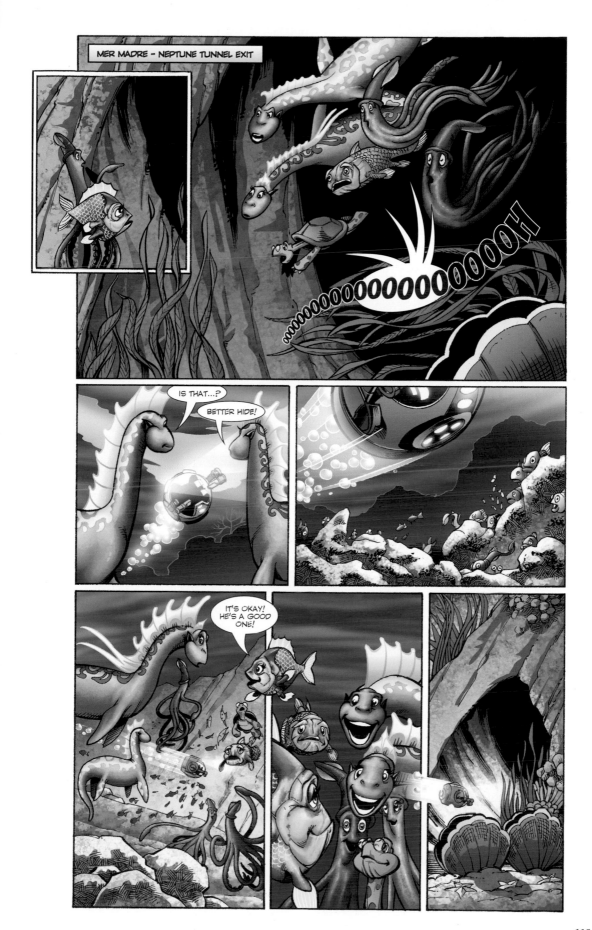

JUST THINK SWEETIE. IF I WERE LEADER, YOU WOULD NEVER HAVE TO WORRY ABOUT DRYWALKERS AGAIN.

I'VE LEARNED THAT *DRYWALKERS* ARE NOT THE ENEMY!

GASP

WHAT WAS THAT?

CHAMP, I'M SORRY.

I'VE BEEN SO AFRAID OF DRYWALKERS, I COULDN'T SEE THAT SOME OF THEM ARE TRYING TO HELP US.

WHEN I REALIZED THAT YOUR FRIEND, WYATT, WAS TRYING TO PROTECT ME FROM THE OTHER DRYWALKERS, I KNEW I HAD BEEN WRONG.

SEE, SHE REALLY IS CRAZY!

SO YOU CAN CONTINUE TO HATE, BUT IT WON'T MAKE YOU SAFER.

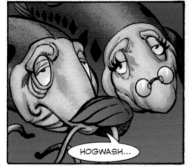

HOGWASH...

WHRRRRRRRRR

WYATT!

YES, I'M HERE TO HELP.

HUH?

118

120

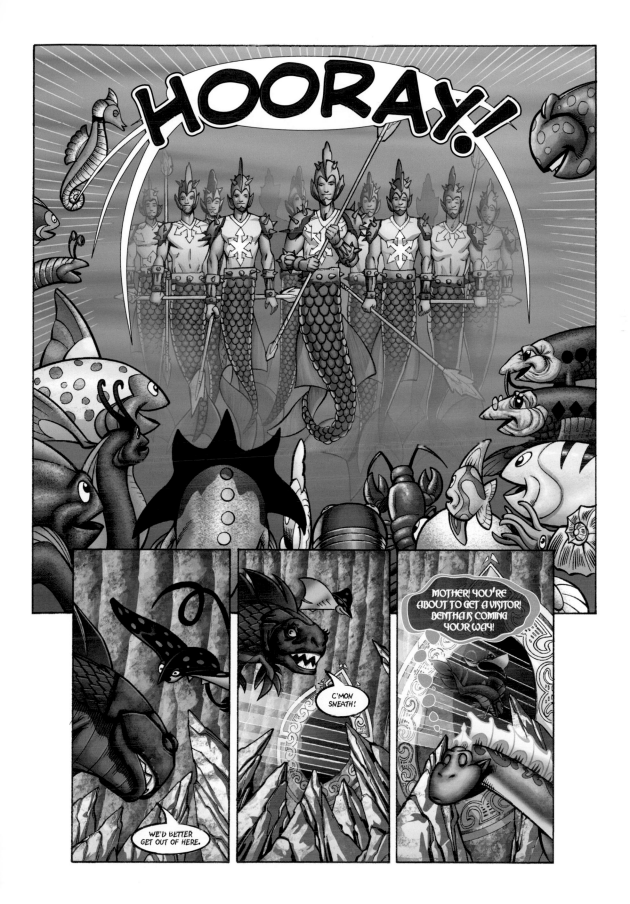

MER MADRE
NEPTUNE TUNNEL EXIT

WE'RE SAFE!

UH OH!

...UNBELIEVEABLE!

HIDE!

LOAD EVERYTHING!

BUT—

DO IT!

STAY HIDDEN!

WHAT DO WE DO NOW?

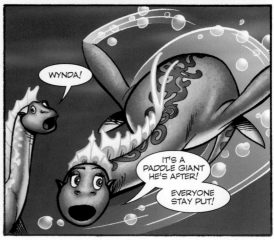

WYNDA!

IT'S A PADDLE GIANT HE'S AFTER!

EVERYONE STAY PUT!

WHAT'S THIS?

R...R...RRRRRRRRRRRRR

THE CREATURES YOU ATTEMPTED TO KILL HAVE SAVED YOUR LIVES.

BUT...THAT'S NOT POSSIBLE.

IT IS POSSIBLE! IN RETURN YOU MUST PROTECT THEM BY NOT REVEALING THEIR EXISTENCE.

BUT HOW CAN WE KEEP A SECRET OF THIS MAGNITUDE?

MY SISTER'S DREAM HAS COME TRUE.

BONDOLAY!

OOF!

I THINK I'M GOING TO CRY.

WE ALL HAVE TO GO SOMETIME.

IT'S TIME FOR YOU TO ARCK, NESSANDRA

I'LL BE BACK SOON, MY FRIENDS.

...A WORLD WITHOUT FEAR.

130

THE HIDDEN LOCH
LEXICON

SOME ANCIENT CREATURES FOUND LIVING IN THE HIDDEN LOCH

CAPROBERYX
(cap-row-bear-ex)
Beryx

An extinct genus of ray-finned fish from the Cretaceous period of Europe and Africa. Fossils have also been found in Kansas.★

COELACANTH
(see-la-canth)
Ceelord

The coelacanth was once thought to be extinct, having lived from the Paleozoic Devonian period until the Cretaceous period. However, in 1938, Courtenay -Latimer rediscovered the first live specimen off the coast of East London, South Africa. Another live specimen was caught in Indonesia in 1998. Coelacanths belong to a group of lobed-finned fish related to Lungfish and certain extinct Devonian fish. It is considered the most endangered order of animals in the world.★

CRYPTOZOOLOGY
(crip-toe-zoo-all-o-gee)

The science of studying "hidden" or rumored animals by exploring local traditions, sightings, tales, and folklore, for evidence of an animal's existence in present time.

DONKLEOSTEUS
(dunk-lee-os-te-us)
Bentha

Dunkleosteus was one of many species of placoderms, a diverse group of armored fishes that dominated aquatic ecosystems during the Devonian period, from 415 to 360 million years ago.
It was considered "the first king of the beasts", with teeth and jaws that could bite a shark in two.
It was 33 feet long and weighed up to four tons.★★

DRYWALKER
(dry-walker)
Wyatt

What the inhabitants of The Hidden Loch call humans.

KRAKEN
(cray-ken)
Krakey

Kraken is a huge legendary sea monster that is believed by many to actually be a giant squid. The giant squid lives in the deepest part of the ocean and is rarely seen. It was first mentioned in the works of Aristotle in the fourth century BC.
The giant squid is a predatory Cephalopod from the family Architeuthidae.
They can grow to a length of 16 to 20 feet. They have eight arms and two longer tentacles. They also have the largest eyes of any living creature and a strong sharp beak that can rip apart almost anything.★

LUNGFISH or
CERATODONTIFORMES
(sara-toe-don-ti-form)
Mon and Gran Lipilung

This ancient species of lungfish can be traced back to the Mesozoic period. They have a lung that can keep them alive out of the water for prolonged periods of time providing they are kept wet.

This species of lungfish have flipper like fins and large scales. ★★★

MER MADRE
(mare ma-dray)

What the inhabitants of the Hidden Loch call the Atlantic Ocean.

PLESIOSAUR
(pleez-ee-o-soar)
Nessandra

Referred to as "Paddle Giants" in the Hidden Loch, these marine reptiles (often thought of as dinosaurs) roamed the oceans during the late Triassic period to the Cretaceous period. They had four long flippers, which were powered by strong muscles attached to wide bony plates and often had long necks. They were capable of breathing air and giving live birth. There are indications they were warm blooded like mammals. ★

SEA TURTLE
Torto

Sea turtles go back to the late Jurassic period and have survived up to the present day. They can be found in all oceans except for the polar regions. Sea turtles are much larger than their land counterparts. They can grow as large as 6 to 9 feet long and up to 1500 pounds in weight. They have a fusiform (tapering at both ends) body which allows them to swim more easily. ★

SKATE FISH
Sneath

Skate fish appeared in the fossil record 150 million years ago. They are similar to stingrays, but are smaller and have a more pointed frontal section. Their fins are divided into two lobes and they swim with their pectoral fins. They mature late and have slow growth rates. ★

★en.wikipedia.org

★★livescience.com

★★★primitivefishes.com

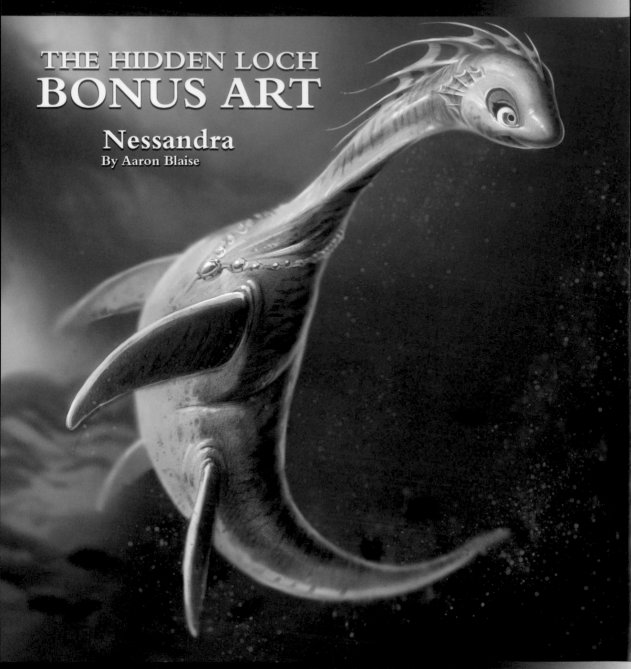

THE HIDDEN LOCH
BONUS ART

Nessandra
By Aaron Blaise

Nessandra

Teen

10 years old

By Claude St. Aubin

Big Ness

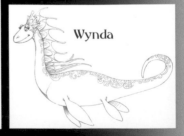

Wynda

Allura
By Aaron Blaise

Allura

By Claude St. Aubin

Allura

Teen

10 years old

Allura

Teen

10 Years Old

Emperians

King Emperian

By Claude St. Aubin

Zapp

By Aaron Blaise

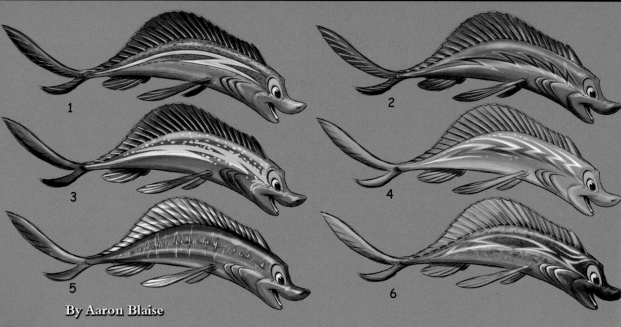

1

2

3

4

5

6

By Aaron Blaise

Zapp

Teen

10 years old

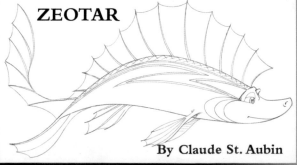

ZEOTAR

By Claude St. Aubin

Champ
By Aaron Blaise

Champ
By Claude St. Aubin

Lochians 1
By Claude St. Aubin

Lochians 2

3
Lochians

Krakey

By Aaron Blaise

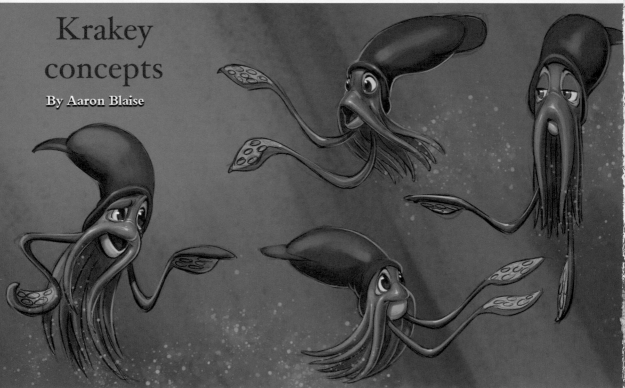

Krakey concepts

By Aaron Blaise

By Claude St. Aubin

By Claude St. Aubin